FOLENS MATHS RAPID RECALL TESTS

Book 5

Hilary Koll

Steve Mills

Folens
Publishers

Acknowledgements

Folens allows photocopying of pages marked 'copiable page' for educational use, providing that this use is within the confines of the purchasing institution. Copiable pages should not be declared in any return in respect of any photocopying licence.

Editor: Hayley Willer   Layout artist: Philippa Jarvis
Cover design: Martin Cross

© 1999 Folens Limited, on behalf of the authors.

Summary of rapid recall objectives from the *Framework for Teaching Mathematics*, published by the DFEE as part of the National Numeracy Stategy.

First published 1999 by Folens Limited, Dunstable and Dublin.
Folens Limited, Albert House, Apex Business Centre, Boscombe Road, Dunstable, LU5 4RL, United Kingdom.
Reprinted 1999.
Reprinted 2000 (twice).

ISBN 1 86202 820–6

Introduction

Rapid Recall Tests and the National Numeracy Framework

This series provides short, sharply focused, photocopiable assessments for each year at Key Stages 1 and 2. These assessments are intended to help teachers monitor the progress their pupils make in relation to the National Numeracy Framework's rapid recall targets. They are to be administered orally to a whole class or group and, as such, aim to help children in their preparation for Key Stage 2 National Mental Maths tests.

The National Numeracy Framework identifies key rapid recall targets to be reached during each year. Book 5 contains 22 tests leading towards the mastery of the end-of-year targets below.

We have labelled the pupil pages with the title 'Unit' rather than 'Test'. This allows individual teachers to indicate to the children a word of their choice, e.g. test/assessment/worksheet/practice.

Test administration

The 'Teacher notes' in each test unit provide the teacher with 15 questions to be delivered orally and answers for quick and easy marking. There is a strong emphasis on the use of National Numeracy Strategy recommended language in each question. The second page in each test unit provides a photocopiable pupil test.

In order to ensure mental recall rather than mental calculation, it is essential that the teacher has control of the pacing of the test.
It is suggested that each question is read twice and approximately 5–10 seconds are allowed for answering.

Regular use of these tests provides essential information as to whether each child is learning and remembering the number facts for that year group. As recommended, children can be closely involved in this monitoring, and feedback from these tests will provide clear information on aspects to be improved.

Summary of rapid recall objectives: Year 5

- Derive quickly or continue to derive quickly:
  - decimals that total 1 (e.g. 0.2 + 0.8) or 10 (e.g. 6.2 + 3.8)
  - all two-digit pairs that total 100 (e.g. 43 + 57)
  - all pairs of multiples of 50 with a total of 1000 (e.g. 350 + 650).

- Know by heart:
  - multiplication facts up to 10 x 10.

- Derive quickly or continue to derive quickly:
  - division facts corresponding to tables up to 10 x 10
  - doubles of whole numbers 1 to 100 (e.g. 78 x 2)
  - doubles of multiples of 10 to 1000 (e.g. 670 x 2)
  - doubles of multiples of 100 to 10 000 (e.g. 6500 x 2)
  - the corresponding halves.

Teacher notes

Questions	Answers
1. What is half of 24?	12
2. What is the product of 3 and 4?	12
3. Write the missing number in the box.	29
4. A football costs £7. How much change would you get from £20?	£13
5. What is 4 multiplied by 5?	20
6. If you have 6 sweets, how many more do you need to get to 20?	14
7. What is double 7?	14
8. Look at the number on the card and divide it by 2.	50
9. 700 plus what, makes 1000?	300
10. Circle the number that is the sum of 9 and 11.	(20)
11. Write the missing number in the box.	0.5
12. A number doubled is 50. Circle the number.	(25)
13. If half of a number is 24, what is the number?	48
14. Circle the number that is one third of 9.	(3)
15. This question paper is torn. What number is missing?	4

Name: _____   **Date:** _____

1. _____

2. [3] [4] _____

3. [   ] + 71 = 100

4.

£7

_____

5. 4 × 5 = [   ]

6.

_____

7. _____

8. [100] _____

9. 700 + [   ] = 1000

10. 19   29   20   99

11. 0.5 + [   ] = 1

12. 100   25   20   15

13. _____

14. 3   18   6

15.

16 + [   ] = 20

Teacher notes

Questions	Answers
1. What is the product of 5 and 4?	20
2. 250 plus what, makes 1000?	750
3. What is half of 42?	21
4. Saleem spends £42 on CDs. How many does he buy?	6
5. Half of a number is 240. What is the number?	480
6. What needs to be added to 13 to make 20?	7
7. What is half of 40?	20
8. Circle the number that is one fifth of 25.	(5)
9. Write the missing number in the box.	22
10. Look at the number shown. Divide this number by 10.	8
11. Write the missing number in the box.	0.1
12. A number doubled is 60. Circle the number.	(30)
13. Circle the number that is the sum of 12 and 6.	(18)
14. What is 70 divided by 7?	10
15. Part of this question paper is torn. What number is missing?	70

Name: _____ **Date:** _____

1.

| 5 | 4 | _____ |

2.

250 + ☐ = 1000

3.

_____

4.

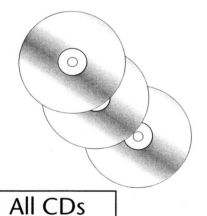

All CDs
£7.00

_____

5.

_____

6.

13 + ☐ = 20

7.

_____

8.

5   1   20   4

9.

100 – ☐ = 78

10.

80

_____

11.

0.9 + ☐ = 1

12.

6   30   120   40

13.

14   18   20   24

14.

_____

15.

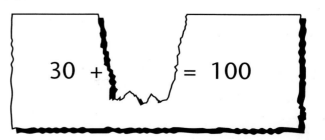

30 + ☐ = 100

Teacher notes

Questions	Answers
1. A number doubled is 46. What is the number?	23
2. Write the missing number in the box.	0.2
3. Circle the number that is one eighth of 80.	⑩
4. A number doubled is 24. Circle the number.	⑫
5. Write the missing number in the box.	9
6. Look at the number on the card and divide it by 5.	11
7. Part of this question paper is torn. What number is missing?	83
8. What needs to be added to 950 to make 1000?	50
9. What is half of 80?	40
10. To visit this historic site each person must pay 8 drachmas. How many drachmas would it cost for 6 people?	48
11. What is 63 divided by 9?	7
12. 200 plus what, makes 1000?	800
13. What is 4 multiplied by 8?	32
14. What is the product of 7 and 3?	21
15. What is 81 divided by 9?	9

Name: _____ **Date:** _____

1.

46 _____

2.

0.8 + ☐ = 1

3.

10 8 18 4

4.

12 6 42 24

5.

18 − ☐ = 9

6.

55 _____

7.

17 + ☐ = 100

8.

_____

9.

_____

10.

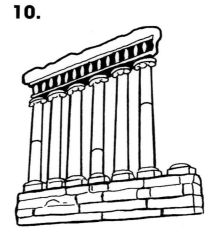

_____

11.

_____

12.

200 + ☐ = 1000

13.

_____

14.

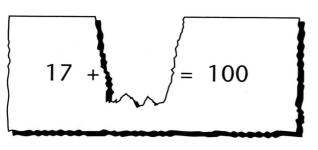 7 3 _____

15.

81 ÷ 9 = ?

_____

Teacher notes

Questions	Answers
1. A number doubled is 50. What is the number?	25
2. A number doubled is 44. Tick the circle that shows the number.	
3. What is half of 34? Circle the answer.	⑰
4. What is the product of 5 and 6?	30
5. 750 plus what, makes 1000?	250
6. Circle the number that is the sum of 4 and 7.	⑪
7. Sam scored half as many points in his second game of pinball. How many did he score in his second game?	9400
8. What is 6 multiplied by 7?	42
9. Write the missing number in the box.	0.7
10. How many pounds did the twins win in total?	£4880
11. Look at the number. Divide it by 5.	9
12. Write the missing number in the box.	5
13. What is half of 28?	14
14. What is 4000 doubled?	8000
15. How many groups of 6 can be made from 36?	6

Name: _____ **Date:** _____

1.

_____

2.

(40) (4) (22) (24)

3.

7   17   14   4

4.

_____

5.

$750 + \boxed{} = 1000$

6.

11   47   3   12

7.

18 800

_____

8.

$6 \times 7 = \boxed{}$

9.

$0.3 + \boxed{} = 1$

10.

Lottery Win!
Twins win **£2440** each

_____

11.

45

_____

12.

$8 \times \boxed{} = 40$

13.

_____

14.

_____

15.

_____

Teacher notes

Questions	Answers

1. What is 49 divided by 7? Circle the answer. — ⑦

2. Look at the number on the card and divide it by 9. — 4

3. What is the product of 3 and 9? — 27

4. Write the missing number in the box — 0.8

5. A number doubled is 220. Tick the number. — ⑪⓪

6. What is 50 divided by 5? Circle the number. — ⑩

7. Write the missing number in the box. — 7

8. How much would it cost for two ice creams? — 144p or £1.44

9. What is 1 subtract 0.8? — 0.2

10. What is half of 360? — 180

11. A dart hitting the white area of the dartboard scores double points. How many points would the dart score? — 96

12. What is the product of 7 and 6? — 42

13. 100 plus what, makes 1000? — 900

14. What is half of 38? — 19

15. Circle the number that is the sum of 6 and 7. — ⑬

Name: _____   **Date:** _____

1.

7   8   6

2.

36

_____

3.

_____

4.

[ ] + 0.2 = 1

5.

(11)   (22)   (210)   (110)

6.

5   50   11   10

7.

56 – [ ] = 49

8.

   Ice cream 72p

_____

9.

1 – 0.8 = [ ]

10.

_____

11.

   48

_____

12.

_____

13.

100 + [ ] = 1000

14.

_____

15.

42   1   13   31

Teacher notes

Questions	Answers
1. Look at the number shown. Divide this number by 3.	1
2. Write the missing number in the box.	5
3. A number doubled is 64. Tick the circle that shows the number.	32
4. Half of a number is 120. Circle the number.	240
5. Circle the number that is one tenth of 70.	7
6. Write the missing number in the box.	0.3
7. This paper is torn. Which number is missing?	6400
8. Subtract 10 from the number on the card.	78
9. What is the the product of 8 and 4?	32
10. How much money will two cups of coffee cost?	132p or £1.32
11. What is half of 34?	17
12. 200 plus what, makes 1000?	800
13. Circle the number that is the sum of 7 and 8.	15
14. What is 9 multiplied by 7?	63
15. What is 1 minus 0.5?	0.5

Name: _____   **Date:** _____

1.

   _____

2.

$9 \times \boxed{} = 45$

3.

4.

12   60   240   24

5.

10   7   17   70

6.

$\boxed{} + 0.7 = 1$

7.

Half of ⌐‾‾⌐ is 3200.

8.

88   _____

9.

_____

10.

   Coffee 66p

_____

11.

_____

12.

$200 + \boxed{} = 1000$

13.

15   56   78   86

14.

$9 \times 7 = \boxed{}$

15.

_____

Teacher notes

Questions	Answers
1. Write the missing number in the box.	0.7
2. Look at the number and divide it by 3.	11
3. Circle the number that is the sum of 13 and 8.	㉑
4. An arrow hitting the white area of the target board scores double points. How many points would the arrow score?	146
5. Double the number on the card is 50. What is the number on the card?	25
6. Part of this sum is missing. What is hidden?	40
7. Tick the numbers that are multiples of 5.	✓ ✓ 20 25
8. What is half of 184?	92
9. 300 plus what, makes 1000?	700
10. What is the product of 8 and 7?	56
11. Write the missing number in the box.	60
12. A number doubled is 160. Circle the number.	⑧⓪
13. Circle the number that is one sixth of 12.	②
14. One of the numbers shown here can be divided exactly into 81, with no remainder. Tick the correct star.	
15. This paper is torn. Which number when doubled gives 12 400?	6200

Name: _____ **Date:** _____

1. + 0.3 = 1

2. 33 _____

3. 21 5 23 22

4.  73

_____

5. ? _____

6. + 60 = 100

_____

7. 16 20 25 51

8. _____

9. 300 + [ ] = 1000

10. _____

11. 70 − [ ] = 10

12. 800 320 80 16

13. 2 6 12 20

14.  2 9 5 10

15. Double _____ is 12 400.

RAPID RECALL MATHS: *Book 5*

Teacher notes

Questions	Answers

1. Circle the number that can be divided exactly by 8 with no remainder.

(56)

2. Write the missing number in the box.

5

3. Write the missing number in the box.

0.9

4. What is half of 88?

44

5. What is the product of 8 and 9?

72

6. Look at the number shown. Divide this number by 4.

10

7. Write the number that is the sum of 7 and 14.

21

8. 2 people win £700 and they split it equally between them. They each get how many pounds?

£350

9. A number doubled is 140. What is the number?

70

10. A number doubled is 42. Tick the circle that shows the number.

(21)

11. A dart hitting the white area of the dartboard scores double points. What does the dart score?

1200

12. 400 plus what, makes 1000?

600

13. Circle the number that is one ninth of 27.

(3)

14. When I divide a number by 7 I get 5. What is the number?

35

15. What is 80 divided by 8? Circle the answer.

(10)

Name: _____   **Date:** _____

1.

56   54   55   58

2.

$4 \times \boxed{} = 20$

3.

$0.1 + \boxed{} = 1$

4.

_____

5.

_____

6.

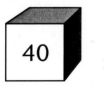   _____

7.

   _____

8.

2 people win £700 and they split it equally between them.

They each get £_____.

9.

_____

10.

(40) (14) (21) (24)

11.

600

_____

12.

$400 + \boxed{} = 1000$

13.

27   9   3

14.

_____

15.

8   18   10   0.8

Teacher notes

Questions	Answers
1. Look at the number in the triangle. Divide this number by 4.	9
2. Write the missing number in the box.	4
3. Circle the number that is one seventh of 42.	⑥
4. A number doubled is 28. Circle the correct number.	⑭
5. Tick the card that can be divided exactly by 4.	☑ 12
6. Which number, when added to 650, makes 1000?	350
7. Part of this question paper is torn. What number is missing?	57
8. What is 30 divided by 6?	5
9. What is the product of 7 and 10?	70
10. This television and video cost £1000 in total. If the video costs £250, how much does the television cost?	£750
11. Write the missing number in the box.	0.2
12. What is half of 64?	32
13. Circle the number that is the sum of 5 and 16.	㉑
14. What is half the number shown?	310
15. How much more is needed to make 1000g?	450g

Name: _____ **Date:** _____

1.  _____	**9.** _____
2. 7 x [ ] = 28	**10.** 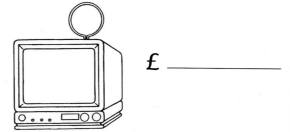 £ _____ 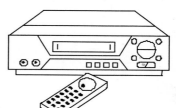 £250
3. 8 7 6 9	
4. 18 14 16 12	
5. 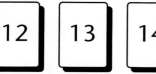 12 13 14 15	**11.** 0.8 + [ ] = 1
6. 650 + [ ] = 1000	**12.** _____
7. 100 – [ ] = 43	**13.** 30 11 21 1 14
	14. 620 _____
8. _____	**15.** 550g _____

Teacher notes

Questions	Answers
1. Circle the number that is the sum of 9 and 7.	(16)
2. What is the product of 8 and 5?	40
3. Look at the number and divide it by 10.	9
4. A dart hitting the white area of the dartboard scores double points. What does the dart score?	240
5. Part of this question is missing. What number is hidden?	37
6. A number doubled is 66. What is the number?	33
7. Circle the number that, when doubled, makes 860.	(430)
8. Write the missing number in the box.	0.2
9. What is half of 52?	26
10. Write the missing number in the box.	15
11. Circle the number that is one sixth of 36.	(6)
12. A number doubled is 48. What is the number?	24
13. 400 plus what, makes 1000?	600
14. How much more money do we need to save to reach £1000?	£950
15. Part of this question paper is torn. What is missing?	45

Name: _____   **Date:** _____

1. 6 16 61 27	**8.** 0.8 +  = 1
2. _____	**9.** _____
3. 90 _____	**10.** 21 − ⬜ = 6
4. 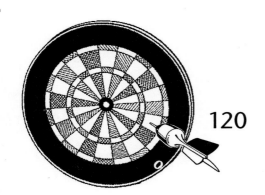 120 _____	**11.** 16 3 6 13
	12. _____
	13. 400 +  = 1000
5. 63 +  = 100 _____	**14.** £50 _____
6. _____	**15.** 100 − 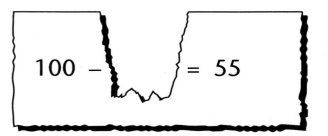 = 55
7. 820 420 430 440	

RAPID RECALL MATHS: *Book 5*

Teacher notes

Questions	Answers
1. What number when doubled makes 48?	24
2. Circle the number that is one tenth of 40.	④
3. What is the product of 8 and 4?	32
4. A number added to 300 makes 1000. What is that number?	700
5. Write the missing number in the box.	5
6. Look at the number and divide it by 6.	3
7. Circle the number that is the sum of 17 and 7.	㉔
8. Part of this sum is hidden. What is missing?	62
9. What is 120 divided by 10?	12
10. Write the missing number in the box.	0.7
11. The next arrow will score double points. How many points will it be worth?	900
12. What is half of 70?	35
13. Tick the card that is half of 2200.	✓ 1100
14. Which number multiplied by 3 equals 21?	7
15. What is one fifth of 45?	9

Name: _____   **Date:** _____

1.

_____

2.

   4   14   10   6

3.

_____

4.

$300 + \boxed{} = 1000$

5.

$6 \times \boxed{} = 30$

6.

    _____

7.

   77   14   27   24

8.

 $+ \ 38 = 100$

_____

9.

$120 \div 10 = \boxed{}$

10.

$0.3 + \boxed{} = 1$

11.

450

_____

12.

_____

13.

| 1000 | 1100 | 120 | 105 |

14.

$3 \times \boxed{} = 21$

15.

    _____

Teacher notes

Questions	Answers
1. Look at the number shown and divide it by 9.	7
2. Circle the number that is the sum of 10 and 8.	⑱
3. Write the missing number in the box.	0.4
4. A number doubled is 800. Tick the circle that shows the number.	✓ ④⓪⓪
5. Write the missing number in the box.	90
6. 200 plus what, makes 1000?	800
7. Part of this question paper is torn. What is missing?	8800
8. What are five sixes?	30
9. What is half of 110?	55
10. This piece of ribbon is 72cm long. How many lengths of exactly 8cm can be cut from it?	9
11. Circle the number that is one third of 30.	⑩
12. Circle the number that is one eighth of 64.	⑧
13. What is the product of 8 and 9?	72
14. What is the total of the two cards?	52
15. What is half the number on the tin?	320

Name: _____   **Date:** _____

1.   63 _____

2.   12   2   18   108

3.   0.6 + [   ] = 1

4.   (500) (600) (400) (300)

5.   100 – 10 = [   ]

6.   _____

7.   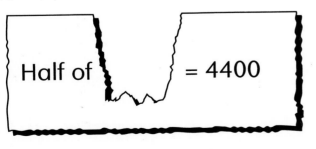 Half of [   ] = 4400

8.   _____

9.   _____

10. 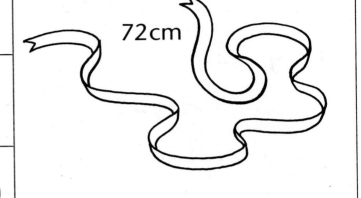 72cm   _____

11.   3   13   30   10

12.   6   18   8   42

13.   _____

14.    20 32 _____

15.   640 _____

RAPID RECALL MATHS: *Book 5*

Teacher notes

Questions	Answers
1. Circle the number that is one fifth of 30.	⑥
2. What is the product of 3 and 7?	21
3. What is half of 120?	60
4. Write the missing number in the box.	0.3
5. A number doubled is 26. What is the number?	13
6. Look at the number shown and add 650 to it.	1000
7. Circle the number that is the sum of 9 and 14.	㉓
8. Tick the number that can be divided exactly by 5.	25
9. Look at the number on the card. Divide this number by 9.	8
10. Write the missing number in the box.	9
11. Double 49 is how many?	98
12. 400 plus what, makes 1000?	600
13. How many times does 6 divide into 60?	10
14. 77 plus what, equals 100?	23
15. What is 30 more than 65?	95

Name: _____ **Date:** _____

1.

    4   5   6   7

2.

_____

3.

_____

4.

$0.7 +$ ☐ $= 1$

5.

_____

6.

350

_____

7.

   5   12   23   25

8.

25   28   32   41

9.

72

_____

10.

$8 \times$ ☐ $= 72$

11.

49

_____

12.

_____

13.

_____

14.

$77 +$ ☐ $= 100$

15.

_____

Teacher notes

Questions	Answers
1. A number doubled is 20. Tick the circle that shows the number.	✓ ⃝10
2. Look at the number and divide it by 9.	8
3. 350 plus what, makes 1000?	650
4. What is half of 140?	70
5. What is the product of 7 and 4?	28
6. Write the missing number in the box.	26
7. Part of this question is missing. Write the missing number.	8
8. Tick the number that divides exactly into 25, with no remainder.	✓ 5
9. Circle the number that is one seventh of 28.	⃝4
10. This sandwich costs £3. How much would it cost for 8 sandwiches?	£24
11. Write the missing number in the box.	0.6
12. Circle the number that is the sum of 3 and 18.	⃝21
13. What is 200 plus 350?	550
14. Half a number is 430. What is the number?	860
15. Write the missing number in the box.	0.2

Name: _____   **Date:** _____

1.
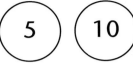
(5) (10) (15) (20)

9.
7   2   14   4

2.

72
_____

10.
£3

_____

3.
_____

4.
(140)
_____

5.
_____

11.
0.4 + [   ] = 1

6.
76 − [   ] = 50

12.
54   15   21   20

7.
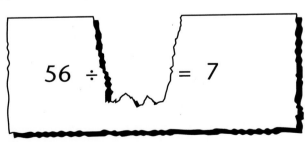
56 ÷ [   ] = 7

13.
200 + 350 = [   ]

14.
_____

8.
3   5   6   7

15.
[   ] + 0.8 = 1

Teacher notes

Questions	Answers

1. What is half of 8000?

4000

2. Circle the numbers that can be divided exactly by 6.

⑫ ⑳60

3. Write the missing number in the box.

0.2

4. Look at the number on the card. Divide this number by 8.

3

5. What is the product of 9 and 4?

36

6. What is half of 160?

80

7. How much more money is needed to reach £100?

£30

8. What number is missing from this sum?

60

9. Two numbers add to make 1000. One number is 450. What is the other?

550

10. Draw an arrow to one tenth of 100.

10

11. A number doubled is 90. Tick the circle that shows the number.

✓
⑤45

12. 250 plus what, makes 1000?

750

13. What is the sum of 7 and 16?

23

14. Write the missing number in the box.

7

15. Which number divides into 35 exactly 5 times?

7

Name: _____ **Date:** _____

1.

_____

9.

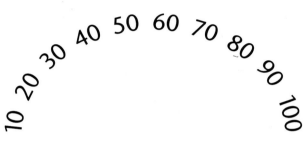

450

_____

2.

12   16   60   62

10.

10 20 30 40 50 60 70 80 90 100

●

3.

0.8 + [   ] = 1

4.

24

_____

11.

45   180   50   35

5.

_____

6.

160

_____

12.

_____

7.

£70

_____

13.

_____

14.

[   ] x 6 = 42

8.

70 − [   ] = 10

15.

_____

Teacher notes

Questions	Answers

1. What is half of 92?

46

2. What is the product of 8 and 3?

24

3. A number doubled is 82. Tick the circle that shows the number.

✓ 41

4. Look at the number shown and divide it by 6.

8

5. 950 plus what, makes 1000?

50

6. Circle the number that is one ninth of 27.

③

7. Part of this sum is hidden. What number is missing?

18

8. This tennis racket costs £7. How much will it cost to buy 6 tennis rackets?

£42

9. What is the sum of 7 and 15?

22

10. Write the missing number in the box.

4

11. An arrow hitting the white area of the target board scores half points. What does the arrow score?

310

12. Write the missing number in the box.

0.5

13. What is half of the number shown?

220

14. Circle two numbers the sum of which is 1.

⓪.4 ⓪.6

15. Which of these numbers can be divided exactly by 7? Tick the star that shows the number.

✓ 21

Name: _____   Date: _____

1.
Half of 92 = _____

2.
_____

3.

(14) (42) (32) (41)

4.

48 _____

5.
_____

6.
3   4   5   6

7.
 + 82 = 100 _____

8.

£7
_____

9.
_____

10.
9 × [ ] = 36

11.

620
_____

12.
[ ] + 0.5 = 1

13.

440 _____

14.
0.5   0.4   0.6   0.7

15.
☆23 ☆24 ☆25 ☆21

Teacher notes

Questions	Answers

1. Which of these numbers can be divided exactly by 4? Circle the answer.

(12)

2. Halve the number.

44

3. A number doubled is 30. Tick the circle that shows the number.

✓ (15)

4. A dart hitting the white area of the dartboard scores double points. How much is this dart worth?

116

5. Part of this sum is missing. What is hidden?

1000

6. What is the product of 9 and 5?

45

7. 150 plus what, makes 1000?

850

8. What is double 350?

700

9. Write the missing number in the box.

0.3

10. Look at the number in the triangle. Divide this number by 8.

5

11. Circle the number that is one sixth of 60.

(10)

12. What is half of 86?

43

13. What is the sum of 9 and 12?

21

14. Tick any of these cards that can be divided exactly by 3.

15. Part of this question paper is torn. What number is missing?

5

Name: _____   **Date:** _____

1.

      12   13   14   15

2.

_____

3.

  20   14   15   60

4.

58

_____

5.

$1100 - 100 =$  _____

6.

_____

7.

_____

8.

_____

9.

$\boxed{} + 0.7 = 1$

10.

 _____

40

11.

  6   60   10   1

12.

_____

13.

$\boxed{9}$ $\boxed{12}$

14.

| 4 | 15 | 6 | 18 | 13 |

15.

$5 \times$ $= 25$

RAPID RECALL MATHS: *Book 5*

Teacher notes

Questions

1. A number doubled is 220. Tick the card that shows the number.

2. 0.9 plus what, makes 1?

3. Multiply 9 by 6.

4. What is half of 220?

5. What is the sum of 13p and 8p?

6. What is the product of 5 and 8?

7. Part of this question paper is torn. What number is missing?

8. Write the missing number in the box.

9. What is the product of 8 and 6?

10. Tick the number that is one quarter of 28.

11. Look at the number and divide it by 4.

12. Write the missing number in the box.

13. Circle the number that divides exactly into 42.

14. Seven eights are how many?

15. Two numbers add to make 1000. One number is 350. What is the other?

Answers

0.1

54

110

21p

40

8

0.3

48

4

62

⑦

56

650

Name: _____   **Date:** _____

1.   110   210   440

2. $0.9 +$ [ ] $= 1$

3.   9   _____

4.   220   _____

5.   _____

6.   _____

7.   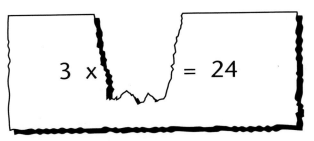 $3 \times$ [ ] $= 24$

8. $0.7 +$ [ ] $= 1$

9.   _____

10.   14   6   18   7

11.   16   _____

12. $38 +$ [ ] $= 100$

13.   7   5   8

14.   _____

15.   350

RAPID RECALL MATHS: *Book 5*

Teacher notes

Questions	Answers
1. What is the product of 3 and 8?	24
2. Look at the number on the card and divide it by 4.	8
3. Write the missing number in the box.	0.8
4. Circle the number that is one sixth of 18.	③
5. 250 plus what, makes 1000?	750
6. Circle the number that can be divided exactly by 9.	⑱
7. What is half of 300?	150
8. 2 people win £3000 and share it equally. How much does each person get?	£1500
9. Write the missing number in the box.	72
10. A number doubled is 28. What is the number?	14
11. The entrance fee to a museum is £6. How much will it cost for 9 people to enter?	£54
12. What is the total of 18 and 8?	26
13. Double the number.	8000
14. 150 plus what, makes 1000?	850
15. What is half of the number in the star?	70

Name: _____ **Date:** _____

1.
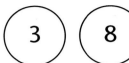 _____

2.
 _____

3.
$0.2 +$ ☐ $= 1$

4.
   6   3   12   2

5.
_____

6.
 14   15   16   17   18   19

7.
 _____

8.

2 people win £3000 and share it equally.

Each person gets £_____ .

9.
$81 - 9 =$ ☐

10.
       28   _____

11.
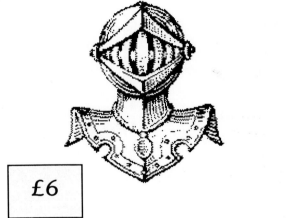

£6   _____

12.
_____

13.
 _____

14.
_____

15.
 _____

Teacher notes

Questions	Answers
1. Circle the number that is one seventh of 35.	⑤
2. What is half the number in the star?	45
3. Write the missing number in the box.	0.6
4. What is half the number in the rectangle?	5000
5. 63 plus what, makes 100?	37
6. What is the sum of 9 and 5?	14
7. Write the missing number in the box.	7
8. 750 plus what, makes 1000?	250
9. What is the product of 8 and 5?	40
10. Look at the number and divide it by 9.	6
11. An arrow hitting the white area of the target board scores double points. How much is the arrow worth?	500
12. What is half of 250?	125
13. What is 4 multiplied by 6?	24
14. A number doubled is 400. Tick the number.	✓ 200
15. Subtract 0.3 from 1.	0.7

Name: _____ **Date:** _____

1. 10 7 5 6	**9.** _____
2.  _____	**10.**  _____
3. 0.4 + ☐ = 1	**11.**  _____
4. ☐ 10 000 _____	
5. 63 _____	
6. _____	**12.**  _____
7. ☐ × 8 = 56	**13.** _____
8. 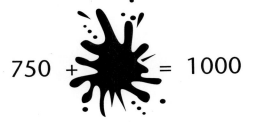 750 + = 1000 _____	**14.** 800 100 200 300
	15. ☐ 1 _____

RAPID RECALL MATHS: *Book 5*

Teacher notes

Questions	Answers

1. What is the sum of 7 and 9?

16

2. What is half of 44?

22

3. A number doubled is 120. Tick the circle that shows the number.

4. 850 plus what, makes 1000?

150

5. Write the missing number in the box.

44

6. What is the total of the two numbers?

85

7. Part of this question paper is torn. What number is missing?

550

8. Look at the number in the star and divide it by 7.

7

9. Write the missing number in the box.

0.9

10. How many 6cm lengths of ribbon can be cut from this 43cm length of ribbon?

7 (1cm remainder)

11. Circle the number that is one third of 60.

⑳

12. How much more money needs to be saved to reach £1000?

£350

13. What is double the amount on the card?

160

14. What is half of 1600?

800

15. What is 6 multiplied by 8?

48

Name: _____   **Date:** _____

1.  | 7 | | 9 | _____

2. 44 _____

3. 120 100 60 80

4. 850 + [ ] = 1000

5. 56 + [ ] = 100

6. 40 45   _____

7. 450 + [ ] = 1000

8. 49 _____

9. [ ] + 0.1 = 1

10. 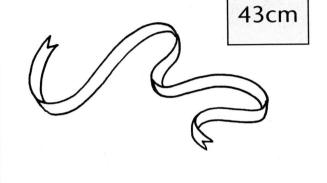 43cm

_____

11. 20 30 10 6

12.  £650   _____

13. 80   _____

14. _____

15. _____

Teacher notes

Questions	Answers

1. What is half of the number shown?

3400

2. A number doubled is 70. Circle this number.

(35)

3. A shop has a half-price sale. What is the new cost of the toy?

£4.40

4. What is the sum of 9 and 8?

17

5. Look at the number and divide it by 5.

8

6. What is half of 2200?

1100

7. 450 plus what, makes 1000?

550

8. Part of this question is hidden. What number is missing?

37

9. 1 minus 0.4 leaves how much?

0.6

10. Circle the number that is one tenth of 90.

(9)

11. How many milkshakes can be bought for £1?

5

12. Divide the number in the star by 2.

31

13. What is the product of 9 and 5?

45

14. What is 54 divided by 9?

6

15. Circle the two numbers that together have a total of 50.

(20) (30)

Name: _____   **Date:** _____

1.  6800 _____	**9.** _____
2. 35 40 30 33	**10.** 5 9 10 12
3. **£8.80** _____	**11.**  Milkshake 20p _____
4. _____	
5. 40 _____	
6. 2200 _____	**12.** 62 _____
7. 450 + ☐ = 1000	**13.** _____
8. 63 +  = 100 _____	**14.** _____
	15. 10 20 30 60

RAPID RECALL MATHS: *Book 5*

Folens Maths

Mathematics teaching in Primary schools has undergone many changes in the last 25 years. None of these has been as significant as the changes brought about by the National Numeracy Strategy launched in September 1999. The focus on whole-class teaching, detailed objectives and an emphasis on children working in groups rather than individually was a radical change from much previous Primary Mathematics practice.

The rapid recall targets contained within the new Curriculum are addressed in this series of books. Whatever Maths scheme is in operation within a school the material in these books will complement it. However, they are also designed to be used in conjunction with two other Folens products.

The *Folens Maths Programme* is a comprehensive teacher resource providing a Mathematics lesson a day linked directly to the Numeracy Strategy.

Folens *Weekly Maths Assessment* provides a fuller assessment of the broader maths objectives, covering the full range of work encountered within the year. These assessments enable the teacher to gain a fuller knowledge of the progress of the individual children across the Mathematics Curriculum.

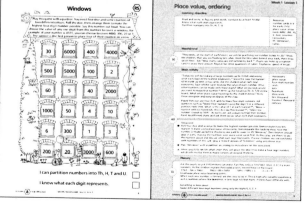